The Visual Guide to

Asperger's Syndrome and Anxiety

by Alis Rowe

Also by Alis Rowe

One Lonely Mind
978-0-9562693-0-0

The Girl with the Curly Hair - Asperger's and Me
978-0-9562693-2-4

The 1st Comic Book
978-0-9562693-1-7

The 2nd Comic Book
978-0-9562693-4-8

The 3rd Comic Book
978-0-9562693-3-1

The 4th Comic Book
978-15086839-7-1

The 5th Comic Book
978-15309879-3-1

Websites:
www.thegirlwiththecurlyhair.co.uk
www.thecurlyhairconsultancy.com
www.theliftingplace.com

Social Media:
www.facebook.com/thegirlwiththecurlyhair
www.twitter.com/curlyhairedalis

The Visual Guide to

Asperger's Syndrome and Anxiety

by Alis Rowe

Lonely Mind Books
London

For people on the autism spectrum
and the people around them

hello

This book is all about anxiety in people on the autistic spectrum.

A lot of people think anxiety is the same for everyone, but I think anxiety for people on the autistic spectrum has different reasons and causes, and consequently it might need to be managed differently.

I hope you enjoy this book.

Alis aka The Girl with the Curly Hair

Contents

WHAT IS ANXIETY?

ANXIETY IS AN UNPLEASANT FEELING THAT WE ALL EXPERIENCE AT TIMES. IT IS A WORD OFTEN USED TO DESCRIBE WHEN WE FEEL 'UPTIGHT', 'IRRITABLE', 'NERVOUS', 'TENSE', OR 'WOUND UP'*

ANXIETY IS ACTUALLY A NATURAL RESPONSE CAUSED BY THE 'FIGHT OR FLIGHT' HORMONE. THE PROBLEM IS WHEN THE ANXIETY IS SO HIGH THAT IT BECOMES DEBILITATING, WHICH IS VERY COMMON FOR AUTISTIC PEOPLE

_____

*   Anxiety. Moodjuice self-help guide. (n.d.). Retrieved from: http://www.moodjuice.scot.nhs.uk/anxiety.asp

ASD AND ANXIETY

THERE ARE SOME SITUATIONS THAT MAKE EVERYBODY ANXIOUS, FOR EXAMPLE:

	NEUROTYPICAL ANXIETY	ASD ANXIETY
TAKING AN EXAM	HIGH	HIGHER
GOING TO THE DOCTOR	HIGH	HIGHER
ACTING IN A PLAY	HIGH	HIGHER
GOING ON A FIRST DATE	HIGH	HIGHER

EVERYONE EXPERIENCES A RESTING LEVEL OF ANXIETY AND A HIGHER LEVEL OF ANXIETY DURING STRESS. HOWEVER, TYPICALLY, AT REST THE ANXIETY OF THE NT WILL BE VERY LOW. THE PERSON WITH ASD AT REST MAY EXPERIENCE SIMILAR ANXIETY TO A STRESSED NT

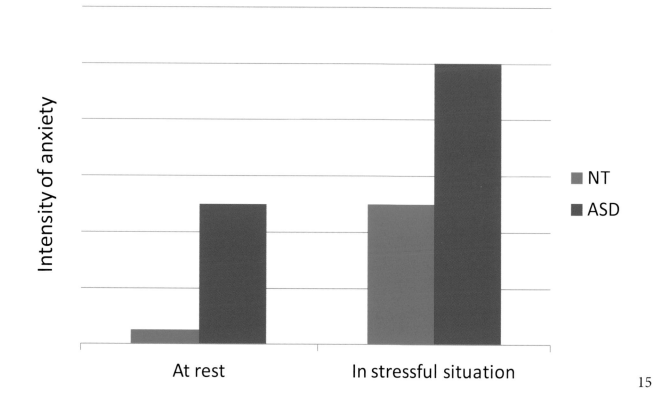

ANXIETY MIGHT INCREASE DURING ADOLESCENCE AS WE ARE DEALING WITH BODY CHANGES BUT ALSO CHANGING RELATIONSHIPS AND A NEW ENVIRONMENT:

SOCIALISING

- MAKING NEW FRIENDS

SECONDARY SCHOOL

- BUSIER, NOISIER ENVIRONMENT
- GETTING USED TO A MORE VARIED TIMETABLE
- ASSOCIATING WITH NEW CLASSMATES AND DIFFERENT TEACHERS

PHYSICAL CHANGES

- GROWING TALLER
- DEVELOPING HIPS AND BREASTS
- BECOMING 'CURVY'
- GROWING HAIR
- PERIODS

EMOTIONAL CHANGES

- INCREASED ANGER
- MOOD SWINGS
- INCREASED SELF-AWARENESS
- STILL FEELING VERY YOUNG
- DIFFICULTY CONNECTING WITH PEERS; LITTLE INTEREST IN BOYS

"It is at puberty and after that metaphorically, the wheels fall off. The person can camouflage their social confusion and use their intellect for integration and imitate simple social interactions but when they become more complex in the teenage years, the person becomes conspicuously less able to cope. The person becomes like Cinderella at the ball at midnight and can socialise for a short while, and is then exhausted and it is then that people recognise the challenges that that person faces."
Professor Tony Attwood

ANXIETY IN PEOPLE ON THE AUTISTIC SPECTRUM TENDS TO OCCUR BECAUSE OF TWO THINGS: SOCIAL AND ENVIRONMENT

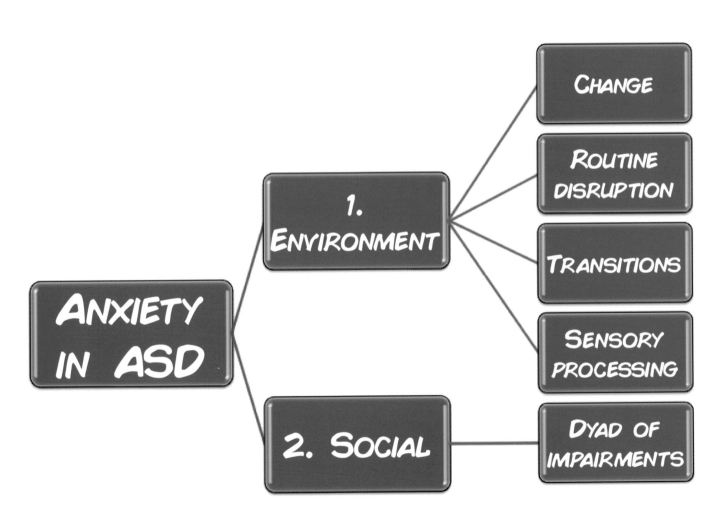

This fits in nicely with DSM-5*, which states that ASD is diagnosed when there are two areas of impairment:

1. Restricted, repetitive patterns of behaviour, interests or activities (environment)

and

2. Social communication and interaction (social)

*   American Psychiatric Association. (2013). Diagnostic and statistical manual of mental disorders (5th ed.). Arlington, VA: American Psychiatric Publishing

Social difficulties that might cause anxiety:

Social	Example of anxiety
Social interaction	Struggling to make friends; struggling to maintain friendships; having different or unusual hobbies so it is difficult to relate to other people
Social communication	Difficulties reading body language; displaying own body language; knowing when to interject into a conversation; knowing what to say; how to respond to someone

Environmental factors that might cause anxiety:

CHANGE

Routine disruption

Transitions

Sensory processing

Because AUTISTIC PEOPLE SEE THE WORLD DIFFERENTLY, IT MEANS THEY REACT TO THINGS DIFFERENTLY TOO

It CAN SOMETIMES BE DIFFICULT THEREFORE, TO EXPLAIN TO NEUROTYPICALS WHY CERTAIN THINGS CAUSE US ANXIETY

Because WE MIGHT GET ANXIOUS OVER DIFFERENT THINGS OR ANXIOUS ABOUT THE SAME THINGS BUT FOR DIFFERENT REASONS, E.G. TAKING AN EXAM...

NT ANXIETY

- THE EXAM QUESTIONS
- DOING WELL
- "HAVE I REVISED ENOUGH?"

ASD ANXIETY

- DISRUPTION TO NORMAL ROUTINE
- DIFFERENT VENUE, DIFFERENT SEAT, GENERALLY A VERY DIFFERENT EDUCATIONAL ENVIRONMENT
- SOCIALISING BEFORE/AFTER THE EXAM
- PROBABLY NOT THE EXAM ITSELF!

THE GIRL WITH THE CURLY HAIR THINKS THAT NEUROTYPICALS TEND TO GET ANXIOUS OVER 'BIG' THINGS THAT HAPPEN EVERY NOW AND THEN...

AND AUTISTIC PEOPLE TEND TO GET ANXIOUS OVER ALL THE 'LITTLE' THINGS THAT HAPPEN THROUGHOUT THE DAY, EVERY SINGLE DAY (WHICH IS A LOT MORE DEBILITATING BECAUSE THE ANXIETY IS THERE ALL THE TIME)

Neurotypical

Anxiety

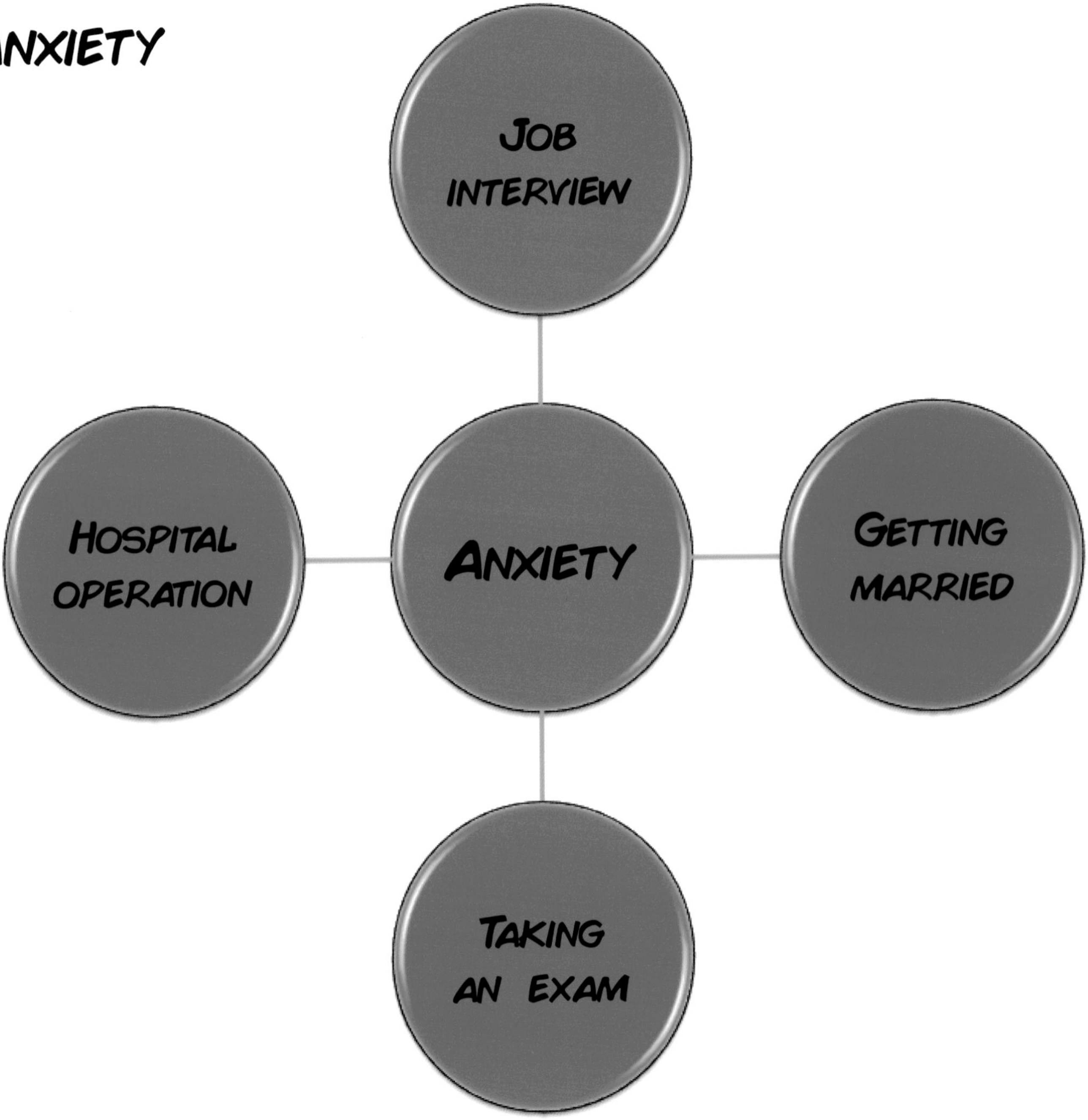

ANXIETY

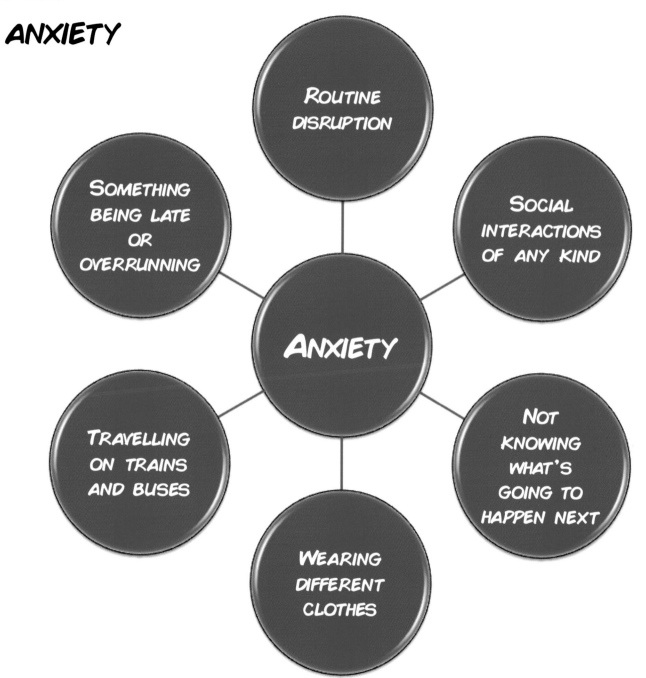

ASD AND SOCIAL ANXIETY

SOCIAL ANXIETY IS ANXIETY FELT IN SOCIAL SITUATIONS

SOME PEOPLE THINK THAT SOCIAL ANXIETY IS DIFFERENT TO SHYNESS

THE GIRL WITH THE CURLY HAIR THINKS THAT SOCIAL ANXIETY IS AN EXTREME LEVEL OF SHYNESS:

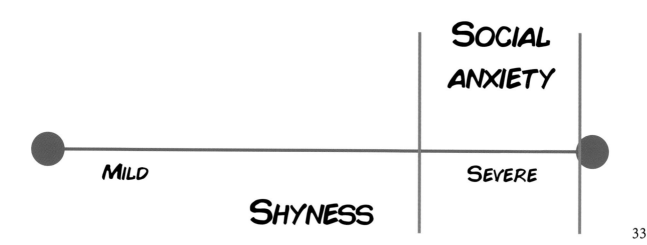

Lots of people on the autistic spectrum are diagnosed with social anxiety before they are diagnosed with ASD

On the surface, social anxiety in neurotypicals vs ASD people looks the same... but if you look deeper, it's actually very different

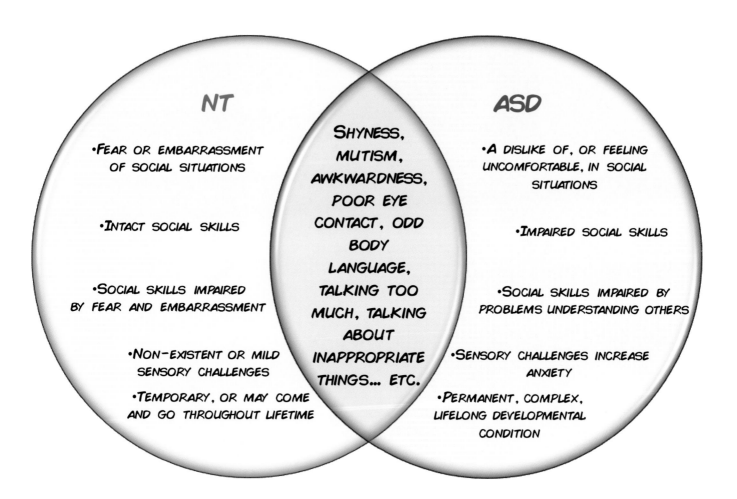

NT

- Fear or embarrassment of social situations
- Intact social skills
- Social skills impaired by fear and embarrassment
- Non-existent or mild sensory challenges
- Temporary, or may come and go throughout lifetime

Shyness, mutism, awkwardness, poor eye contact, odd body language, talking too much, talking about inappropriate things... etc.

ASD

- A dislike of, or feeling uncomfortable, in social situations
- Impaired social skills
- Social skills impaired by problems understanding others
- Sensory challenges increase anxiety
- Permanent, complex, lifelong developmental condition

One key thing to understand is that, in times of social stress, the NT will have the social skills to solve the problem, the ASD person won't

SOCIAL ANXIETY IN AUTISTIC PEOPLE IS MOSTLY CAUSED BY THE DYAD OF IMPAIRMENTS. THE GIRL WITH THE CURLY HAIR THINKS THAT THE DYAD OF IMPAIRMENTS CAUSES A GLASS JAR TO EXIST AROUND EVERY AUTISTIC PERSON:

Examples of thoughts inside social situations for The Girl with the Curly Hair who has social anxiety:

Examples of thoughts inside social situations for A Neurotypical Person who has social anxiety:

Social anxiety in ASD looks like it comes mostly because of the dyad of impairments (which neurotypicals do not have)

So although both autistic people and neurotypical people can have social anxiety, their thoughts are likely to be quite different

Social anxiety in ASD may therefore require different treatment strategies

How anxiety affects behaviour

When our anxiety is very high, it can make us react in extreme ways. Two of these responses are 'Fight' and 'Flight' and the lesser known response is 'Freeze'

FIGHT

- Loss of temper
- Saying something back
- Irritability or aggression
- Defensiveness
- Meltdown

FLIGHT

- Avoidance
- Leaving the area
- Running away
- Panic attack

FREEZE

- Dissociation
- Numbness
- Giving up easily
- Being unable to speak (mutism)
- Isolating ourselves
- Shutdown

The Freeze response

One of the most difficult aspects of the 'Freeze' response is that A PERSON IS UNABLE TO RECEIVE HELP FROM OTHERS, THE PERSON MAY NOT BE ABLE TO DO THINGS TO HELP THEMSELVES, AND THEY MAY BE MORE LIKELY TO RUMINATE OVER PROBLEMS INSTEAD OF FINDING SOLUTIONS FOR THEM

THE WAY A PERSON FEELS WILL AFFECT THE WAY THEY BEHAVE*, I.E.

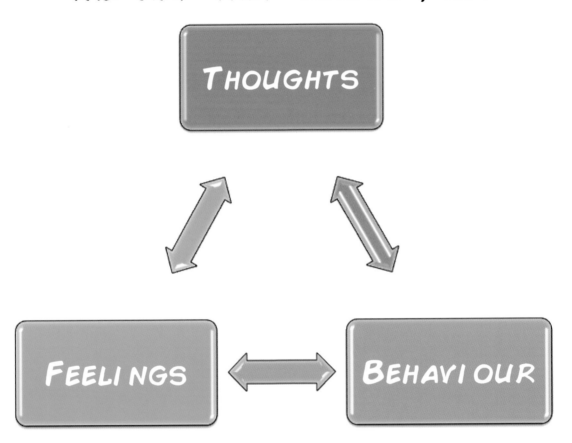

UNUSUAL, CHALLENGING OR 'ODD' BEHAVIOURS MAY INDICATE THAT A PERSON IS FEELING ANXIOUS

*   Cognitive behavioural therapy (CBT). (n.d.). Retrieved from: http://www.nhs.uk/Conditions/Cognitive-behavioural-therapy/Pages/Introduction.aspx

Here are some behaviours that are commonly observed in PEOPLE WITH ASD:

REFUSING TO COMPLY	AGGRESSION AGAINST OTHERS	SELF-HARMING
DEMANDING SAMENESS	STRANGE OR ODD RITUALS	STIMMING
BEING CONTROLLING	RESISTING ASSISTANCE OR DIRECTION	

OFTEN, THE UNDERLYING REASON FOR THESE BEHAVIOURS IS ANXIETY!

Strategies for managing anxiety

"How do I know when I am anxious?"

Firstly, it's very important to learn to recognise when you are anxious

The Girl with the Curly Hair always used to feel anxious but never realised what anxiety was or what it felt like

Identifying signs can be a good place to start for recognising anxiety, for example:

NOT BEING ABLE TO SPEAK

EXCESSIVE BLINKING

HEART BEATING VERY FAST

BLUSHING

ROCKING

HAND FLAPPING

GOING TO THE TOILET A LOT

PACING

IDENTIFYING SYMPTOMS (HOW WE FEEL OR HOW WE ARE EXPERIENCING THINGS) ARE ANOTHER GOOD INDICATOR:

THEN... FOR MANY PEOPLE ON THE AUTISTIC SPECTRUM, HAVING A ROUTINE IS ONE OF THE BEST THINGS SOMEONE CAN DO IN ORDER TO FEEL LESS ANXIOUS

IF THINGS ARE PREDICTABLE, AN AUTISTIC PERSON IS LIKELY TO FEEL MUCH MORE SECURE...

Use a daily timetable

Timetables create structure and routine which take away uncertainty and help to make daily life more predictable

7AM	8AM	9AM	10AM	11AM	12PM	1PM	2PM	3PM	4PM
Walk the dog	Breakfast	Work	Work	Work	Lunch	Work	Work	Work	Gym

MARK OFF THE DAYS

CROSS OFF THE DAYS AS THEY PASS SO THAT THE PERSON CAN SEE HOW CLOSE THEY ARE GETTING TO A PARTICULARLY ANXIETY-PROVOKING EVENT, SUCH AS A HOLIDAY

1ST	2ND	3RD	4TH	5TH	6TH	7TH	8TH	9TH
X	X	X	X	X	X	X	X	HOLIDAY

NOTE: FOR SOME PEOPLE HOWEVER, THE COUNTDOWN IS MORE ANXIETY-PROVOKING THAN BEING GIVEN VERY SHORT NOTICE

Schedule smartly

If we schedule the most anxiety-provoking task to take place at the beginning of our day, it can reduce the time spent worrying

For example, an event at 8am means only two 'blocks' of anxiety compared to eight blocks of anxiety if the same event were scheduled for 2pm:

THE NIGHT BEFORE	7AM	8AM	9AM
ANXIETY	ANXIETY	ANXIETY-PROVOKING EVENT	RECOVERY

THE NIGHT BEFORE	7AM	8AM	9AM	10AM	11AM	12PM	1PM	2PM	3PM
ANXIETY	ANXIETY	ANXIETY	ANXIETY	ANXIETY	ANXIETY	ANXIETY	ANXIETY	ANXIETY-PROVOKING EVENT	RECOVERY

Use visual timetables

Many autistic people like to visualise what is going to happen

A sequence of pictures showing what is going to happen can be helpful, for example at bedtime the routine is brushing teeth-having a bath-going to bed:

Use sequences

Always have an idea of what is going to happen now and what is going to happen next, for example:

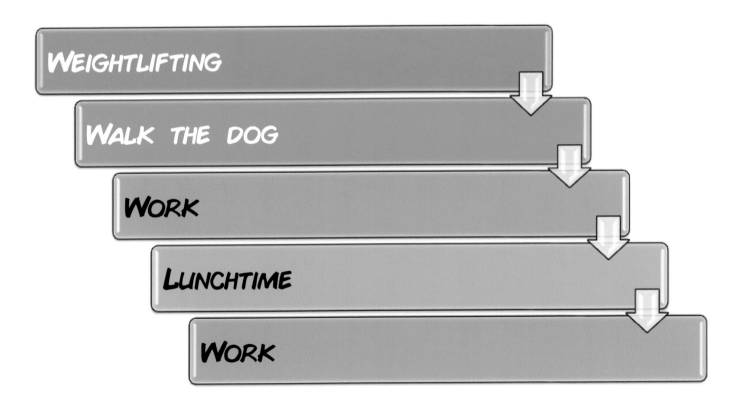

Weightlifting

Walk the dog

Work

Lunchtime

Work

Change times for sections

Time is important to MANY PEOPLE but the world does not always run exactly to time (things overrun, things start late)

It might be helpful to think about getting tasks done in terms of 'sections' in the day rather than at exact 'times'. So for example, instead of:

Time	Task
6.30 AM	Weightlifting
7.30 AM	Walking the dog
9 AM	Doctor's appointment
12 PM	Task B
2 PM	Task C
6 PM	Task D

...MIGHT IT BE LESS ANXIETY-PROVOKING AND MORE REALISTICALLY ACHIEVABLE TO THINK OF SOME TASKS AS HAPPENING 'IN THE MORNING', SOME 'IN THE AFTERNOON' AND SOME 'IN THE EVENING' INSTEAD?

USING 'SECTIONS' RATHER THAN EXACT TIMES CREATES SOME FLEXIBILITY AND BETTER ALLOWS FOR DISRUPTIONS THAT MAY OCCUR BEYOND OUR CONTROL... ULTIMATELY REDUCING A PERSON'S ANXIETY

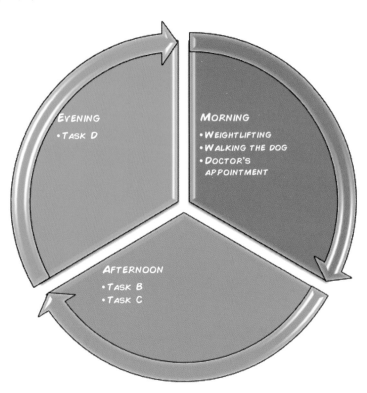

EVENING
•TASK D

MORNING
•WEIGHTLIFTING
•WALKING THE DOG
•DOCTOR'S
 APPOINTMENT

AFTERNOON
•TASK B
•TASK C

Plan in advance but not too far in advance

Plans can help many AUTISTIC PEOPLE but be aware that the more plans there are, the more things there are to think about, and the more overwhelming life can feel

THE GIRL WITH THE CURLY HAIR personally only prefers to have a detailed plan of the day ahead and cares far less about what is happening in the future

SHE FINDS IT LESS ANXIETY-PROVOKING JUST TO LIVE AND FOCUS ON THE PRESENT MOMENT...

REST OF THE WEEK: ROUGH AWARENESS OF WHAT IS HAPPENING

TODAY: LOTS OF DETAIL AND PLANNING

TOMORROW: KNOWLEDGE OF WHAT IS HAPPENING

BEYOND: DON'T WANT TO THINK ABOUT IT

THE MORE PLANS, THE MORE POTENTIAL CHALLENGES AHEAD, THE MORE ANXIETIES, THE MORE HEADSPACE TAKEN UP...

Know start and end time

Find out when a meeting, task or activity, etc. is going to end. It is common to know when something is going to start, but knowing when it's going to finish is just as important

Either we can ask for the expected duration or specify an end time ourselves

BE CLEAR WHEN SOMETHING HAS ENDED

TIMERS CAN HELP THE PERSON "SEE" THE RATE OF THE PASSING OF TIME

PHYSICALLY CROSS IT OFF ON THE CALENDAR OR TIMETABLE

USE A STOP SIGN

WRITE THE EXPECTED END TIME ON A PIECE OF PAPER OR ON A WHITE BOARD

WRITE 'FINISH'

COVER OVER THE WORK WITH A PIECE OF BLANK PAPER (OR TURN TO A NEW, BLANK PAGE)

PUT THE WORK INTO A BOX THAT SAYS 'FINISHED'

AGREE TO DO SOMETHING FOR ONLY A CERTAIN NUMBER OF TIMES

Know the duration of things

As an example, in a P.E. class, the teacher could specify the duration of each aspect of the lesson:

Task	Schedule
Getting changed	5 minutes
Warm up	Do 5 press ups and 5 lunges
Main exercise	Run three times round the field
Cool down	Stretch legs for 30 seconds each
Getting changed	5 minutes

Manage transitions

Sometimes a person might benefit from physically making a transition to help them transition from one activity to another, for example going out of a room and coming back in before starting a new piece of work. Going through a play tunnel, or having different rooms for different tasks

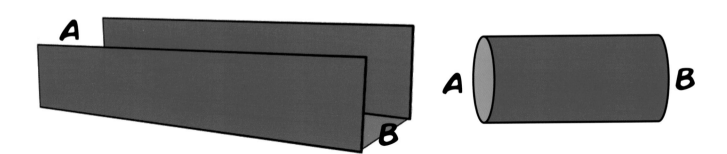

Use tactile/sensory items

People with **ASD** may be overly affected by their senses (sight, sound, touch, smell, etc.)

Think about any items someone could use to make them feel more comfortable, e.g.

Weighted blankets
Noise-reducing earplugs
Headphones (even if not listening to music)
A bottle of lavender oil
Fidget toys/keyrings
Chair bands
Wobble cushions
Stress balls

Identify triggers (the things that make you anxious)

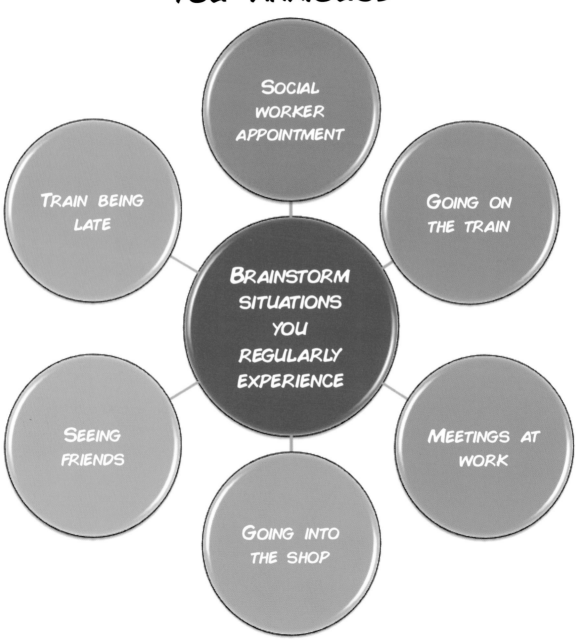

THE GIRL WITH THE CURLY HAIR REALLY LIKES THE VOLCANO CONCEPT:

THIS

EXPLODE

THIS MAKES ME

THIS MAKES ME UNSETTLED

THIS DOESN'T BOTHER ME AT ALL

MAKES ME

VERY ANXIOUS

Apply The Volcano Concept to each trigger!

Tools such as The Volcano Concept allow you to really *PINPOINT* which aspects of a situation are unbearable and think about the ways these could be made a bit easier

It also shows you that no situation is completely *ALL* bad

There might be some difficult parts, but there may be good parts too

Situation – Seeing friends	This doesn't bother me at all	This makes me unsettled	This makes me very anxious	This makes me explode
The location		X		
Duration of socialising		X		
Not knowing what to say			X	
Making eye contact		X		
Being left out			X	

I could ask them lots of questions instead of talking about me!

I could make a list of things I could talk about, in advance

I could see my friends one to one instead of in a group

71

Stay calm

When we feel anxious, we could consider

1. Removing ourselves from the trigger

or

2. Removing the trigger from ourselves

Here are some general calming strategies we can use to reduce anxiety in daily life:

TAKE A BREAK

- *TOILET CUBICLES*
- *GO OUTSIDE*
- *IMAGINE SOMEWHERE RELAXING*

BE MINDFUL

- *DO DEEP BREATHING EXERCISES*
- *TAKE NOTE OF YOUR ENVIRONMENT (BE 'PRESENT')*

CALM YOUR SENSES

- *NOISE REDUCING HEADPHONES*
- *LISTEN TO RELAXING MUSIC*
- *PUT UP HOOD*
- *PLAY WITH STRESS BALL/TOY*
- *DRAW OR COLOUR A PICTURE IN A BOOK*

ALLOW OTHERS TO HELP

- *STAY WITH ONE PERSON*
- *ASK THEM TO ARRANGE FOR YOU TO GET HOME*
- *ASK THEM TO MAKE AN EXCUSE FOR YOU*
- *ASK THEM TO TAKE OVER WHAT YOU ARE DOING*

PLAN IN ADVANCE

- *ROUTES/JOURNEYS*
- *PUBLIC TRANSPORT CONNECTIONS*
- *START/END TIMES*
- *MONTHLY CALENDAR VIEW*
- *DO THINGS EARLY IN THE DAY*

Traffic Light Cards

It is not always easy to express how we are feeling, especially when we are anxious. We can make our own coloured cards and show them to others when we start to feel anxious. The cards have a pre-agreed solution written on them, e.g.

"I am OK."

1. "I need to find a person to talk to and ask for help
2. I need to use a calming method, e.g. Quiet space, music, headphones, etc."

"I am having a meltdown. I need my parent/guardian. Their contact details are..."

AUTISM ALERT CARDS

THESE ARE ALSO USEFUL TO SHOW PEOPLE WHEN WE ARE FEELING ANXIOUS OR WHEN WE ARE HAVING DIFFICULTY COMMUNICATING

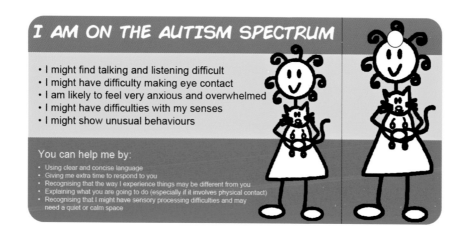

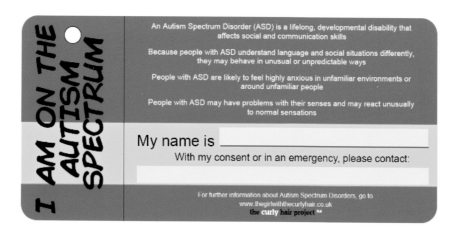

MANAGING ANXIETY IN SOCIAL SITUATIONS

Socialise inside structure

Unstructured social situations can cause a huge amount of anxiety...

OTHER PEOPLE CAN HELP BY GIVING LOTS OF INFORMATION ABOUT WHAT IS GOING TO HAPPEN AND THE AUTISTIC PERSON CAN HELP THEMSELVES BY LEARNING TO ASK FOR THIS INFORMATION

Here are some examples of structured vs unstructured social situations

Structure	Less structure
• Work	• Work (lunch time/after work drinks)
• Lessons at school	• School (playground/break time/before and after school)
• Board games	
• Reading club	• Parties
• Gym	• Club/bar/pub
• Walking the dog	• Going to someone's house
• Cycling to a destination	
• "Pass the Parcel"	

If you're thinking about participating in an unstructured situation, think about

HOW YOU COULD CREATE MORE STRUCTURE TO THOSE SITUATIONS BY FINDING OUT MORE INFORMATION ABOUT THEM, ENSURING AN END TIME... ETC.

Declining invites

Always remember, you do not have to say yes

If something makes you very anxious, it's **OK** not to do it!

There are however, some ways you can politely decline, to ensure that you are invited again and to ensure THE OTHER PERSON knows you appreciated being thought of (most people love to be invited, even if they never actually go along)

TELL THEM AS SOON AS YOU CAN

- IT IS POLITE TO RESPOND AS SOON AS YOU CAN SO THEY CAN MAKE ALTERNATIVE ARRANGEMENTS
- IF YOU CAN'T MAKE UP YOUR MIND, JUST SAY "NO"

BE CLEAR

- SAY "NO" RATHER THAN "MAYBE" SO AS NOT TO LEAD THEM ON/GIVE FALSE HOPE
- DON'T JUST NOT TURN UP

GIVE A REASON (BUT YOU DON'T HAVE TO)

- "I HAVE ASD AND I FIND SOCIAL SITUATIONS VERY HARD"
- "I HAVE SENSORY PROCESSING ISSUES AND BUSY SITUATIONS MAKE ME FEEL OVERWHELMED"
- IT IS OK TO TELL A WHITE LIE, SUCH AS "I AM BUSY THAT DAY/EVENING" OR "I'M NOT FEELING WELL"

THANK THEM FOR THE INVITE

- IT IS POLITE TO THANK THEM FOR THINKING OF YOU
- LET THEM KNOW YOU ARE GRATEFUL TO BE ASKED
- LET THEM KNOW TO CONTINUE TO ASK YOU IN THE FUTURE, IN CASE YOU ONE DAY CHANGE YOUR MIND

DON'T FEEL BAD ABOUT YOUR DECISION

- IT DOES NOT MATTER IF YOU DON'T GO TO A PARTY/SOCIAL EVENT
- YOUR WELL BEING COMES FIRST
- YOU ARE MORE LIKELY TO MAKE OTHERS HAPPY IF YOU ARE HAPPY
- "FUN" IS RELATIVE - WHAT ONE PERSON FINDS FUN, ANOTHER MAY WELL FIND STRESSFUL

Always have a 'get away' for every social situation

Plan in advance the things you could say if you feel yourself getting anxious and needing to leave, e.g.

Generic excuses to help end a conversation

- "I'm in a bit of a rush"
- "I need to go and make a phone call/meet someone now"
- "I'm late for something"
- "I haven't had lunch yet"
- "I've got an early start tomorrow"
- "I need some fresh air"

Shift your focus

Shifting your focus from yourself to what is going on around you can take your mind off how anxious you are feeling, e.g.

- How might another person be feeling?
- What are they talking about?
- What is going on if you look outside the window?
- Is there anything practical you could be doing right now?
- Can you send a text message?
- Can you help lay the table?

Thinking about how bad the situation is and how much you want to get away can actually make you feel worse

There is a saying which goes something like "The more you focus on something, the more significant it becomes"

Try not to focus so much on your own thoughts, feelings, symptoms, etc. ...

INTERNAL
- Thoughts
- Physical signs
- Feelings

EXTERNAL
- Another person
- A task
- The environment

Set an end time...
or have an end goal

Socialising with an end goal can reduce a lot of anxiety as you know in advance when the social situation is going to end

Playing a board game, having lunch together, going on a bike ride to [place] and back home, doing a workout together in the gym, an hour walking the dog... etc.

Make use of time! Time can be a convenient end goal

Always establish exactly how long you plan to socialise before the socialising happens!

Summary

Anxiety might have different causes in NT vs ASD, therefore there might be different things to think about, and different sorts of strategies to use

Work out what your triggers are and come up with strategies you can use — there are some things you can do yourself as well as things others can do to help you

Many thanks for reading

Other books in The Visual Guides series at the time of writing:

Asperger's Syndrome
Asperger's Syndrome: Meltdowns and Shutdowns
Asperger's Syndrome in 5-8 Year Olds
Asperger's Syndrome in 8-11 Year Olds
Asperger's Syndrome in 13-16 Year Olds
Asperger's Syndrome in 16-18 Year Olds
Asperger's Syndrome for the Neurotypical Partner
Asperger's Syndrome: Social Energy
Asperger's Syndrome: Helping Siblings
Asperger's Syndrome and Puberty
Asperger's Syndrome: Meltdowns and Shutdowns (2)
Adapting Health Therapies for People on the Autism Spectrum
Asperger's Syndrome and Emotions
Asperger's Syndrome and Communication

New titles are continually being produced so keep an eye out!